Biology CE/KS3
Topic Booklet

Plants & Photosynthesis

- Read, engage and learn!

- Full colour, illustrated Topic Booklet.

- Glossary, Active Learning Game & Flashcards.

- Ideal for ISEB 13+ Common Entrance and KS3 pupils.

This Oaka™ Books Topic Booklet goes hand in hand with the Active Learning Pack on this topic. This also includes a Write Your Own Notes Booklet, an Active Learning Game and Question & Answer Flashcards.

Fresh Focus on Learning

Oaka™ BOOKS

Plants & Photosynthesis Glossary

 **Biomass:** Material from living plants or recently living plants and animals.

 **Diffusion:** Particles move from an area of high concentration to make an even spread.

 **Biofuel:** Fuel made from sugars or plants.

 **Fertile Soil:** Soil with lots of minerals.

 **Biological Catalysts (enzymes):** Speed up chemical reactions.

 **Fossil Fuels:** Made from plants and animals that died millions of years ago.

 **Carbon Cycle:** Shows how carbon is used in photosynthesis and put back during respiration, death & decay.

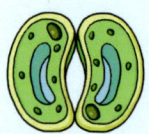 **Guard Cells:** Plant cells with a thick cell wall on one side. They curve like a banana when they swell up.

 **Carbon Dioxide:** A gas produced when burning fuels and during respiration. Used by plants in photosynthesis.

 **Glucose:** A sugar made by plants during photosynthesis.

 **Cell Wall:** The rigid layer around **plant cells**. It gives strength to the cells.

 **Large Vacuole:** A sac filled with cell sap. It swells up and helps make **plant cells** rigid.

 **Chlorophyll:** The green matter in leaves. It absorbs light energy during photosynthesis.

 **Magnesium:** A chemical element used by plants to make chlorophyll.

 **Chloroplasts:** Found in **plant cells**. They contain chlorophyll.

 **Membrane:** A thin layer that surrounds all cells. It lets certain things in and out (semi-permeable).

 **Crude Oil:** Thick, black liquid fossil fuel.

 **Minerals:** Solid matter like rocks. They are not made from plant or animal matter.

Plants & Photosynthesis Glossary

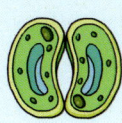
Mitochondria (mit-o-kon-dree-a): Small parts of cells that give out energy from glucose.

Photosynthesis (foto-sin-th-sis): Process used by plants to turn light energy from the sun into chemical energy.

MRS GREN: Living Processes: Movement, Respiration, Sensitivity, Growth, Reproduction, Excretion, Nutrition.

Respiration: The process of releasing energy, trapped in glucose, using oxygen.

Nitrates: Found in soil. They are needed by plants to make proteins.

Rock Cycle: How rocks are formed and eroded.

Nitrogen Cycle: Shows how nitrogen is taken out of the air, by plants and lightening, and then later put back.

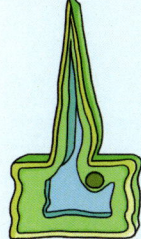
Root Hair Cell: A special plant cell that has a **large surface area**, to take up water and minerals.

NPK Fertilisers: These contain nitrogen, phosphate and potassium salts needed by plants.

Starch: Made from lots of glucose molecules. Plants store glucose as starch.

Nucleus: Controls what happens inside all cells.

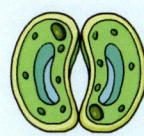
Stomata (sto-ma-ta): Tiny holes in the leaf. They let carbon dioxide in. Water goes out through stomata.

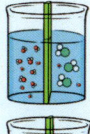
Osmosis: Water moves from an area of high concentration to a low concentration through a semi-permeable membrane.

Transpiration: Water loss from plants. In animals we call it sweating!

Palisade Cells: Plant cells that contain lots of chloroplasts. They give leaves their green colour.

Wax Cuticle: The waterproof layer on the outside of leaves. It helps to stop water loss by evaporation.

Plant Cells

1 Animal Cells

- **All** cells have a **membrane** keeping the cell together.

- They have a **nucleus** to control what the cell does.

- **Mitochondria** give the cell energy.

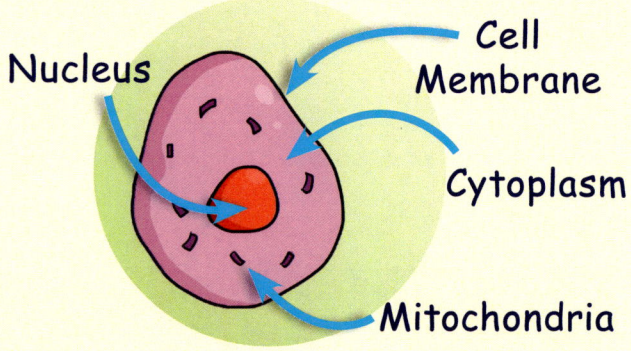

Nucleus
Cell Membrane
Cytoplasm
Mitochondria

2 Plant Cells Have Extras..

- A **cell wall** to help keep its shape.

- **Chloroplasts** containing **chlorophyll** for **photosynthesis**.

- A **large vacuole** to help make the cell rigid.

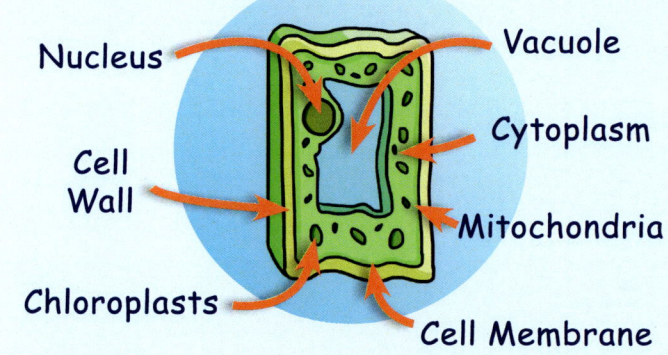

Nucleus
Cell Wall
Chloroplasts
Vacuole
Cytoplasm
Mitochondria
Cell Membrane

3 Plants Don't Have Bones!

- Animals use bones to keep their shape. Plants use **cell walls** and **large vacuoles**.

- Water moves into a plant cell by **osmosis**. This makes the cell swell up.

4 Different Plant Cells

- Plant cells are different shapes and sizes.

- Plants have **specialised cells** to do special jobs.

- **Root hair cells** have a **large surface area** to **absorb** water and minerals.

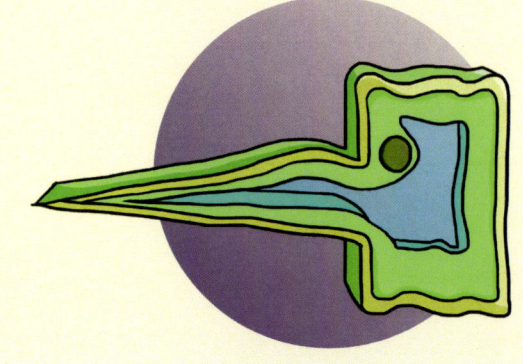

Plant Cells

5 Palisade Cells

- **Palisade cells** have lots of **chloroplasts** to absorb sunlight.

- There are lots of **palisade cells** in leaves.

- **Palisade cells** look like building blocks.

6 Guard Cells & Stomata

- **Guard cells** work in **pairs** making little holes in leaves called **stomata.**

- They let air in and out.

- When **guard cells** swell up they **open** when they **shrink** they **close.**

Gas diffuses through the stomata.

7 Using The Sun's Energy

- Plants use the energy from **sunlight** to make their own food.

- This is called **photosynthesis.**

- Plants are at the start of all food chains.

- Plants need **carbon dioxide** for photosynthesis.

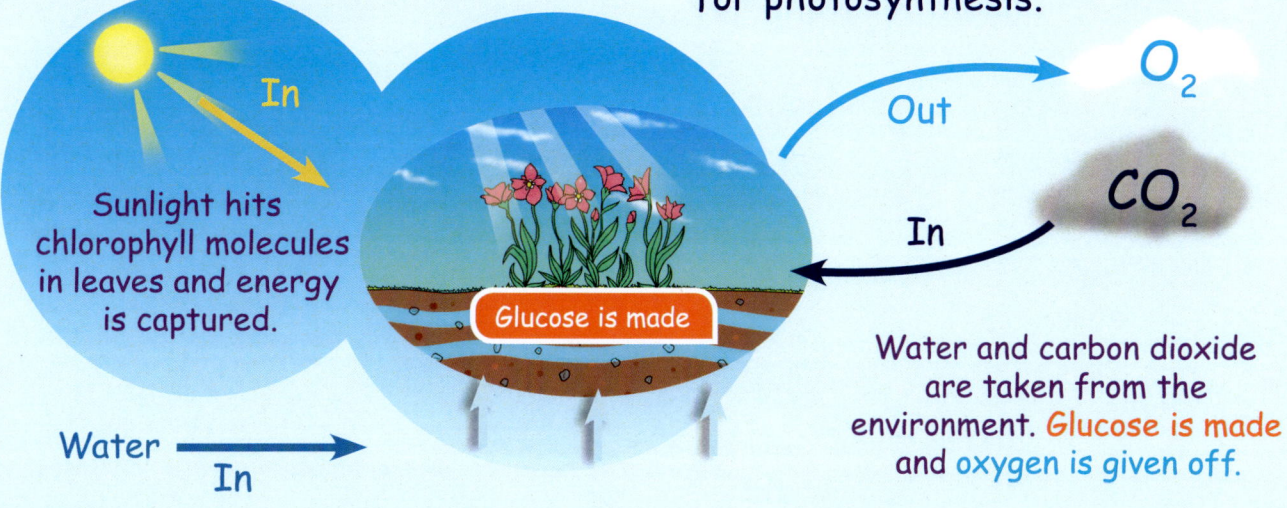

In

Sunlight hits chlorophyll molecules in leaves and energy is captured.

Glucose is made

Water ⟶ In

Out

O_2

CO_2

In

Water and carbon dioxide are taken from the environment. Glucose is made and oxygen is given off.

Plants & Photosynthesis

8   Putting It All Together

Photosynthesis is important!

- Plants **use carbon dioxide** from the air.

- Plants **make the oxygen** we breathe.

- Plants **make the food** we eat.

- Will talking to plants make them grow quicker?

- Think about **respiration!**

Carbon Dioxide (CO_2) **+** Water (H_2O) → (Light Energy / Chlorophyll) Glucose **+** Oxygen (O_2)

9   Water

- Plants need water for **photosynthesis** and to keep their shape.

- If a plant wilts it can't point its leaves towards the sun.

- **P**hotosynthesis slows or stops!

10   Moving Water Around

- Plants have **tubes** to move food, water and minerals around.

- **Phloem** tubes carry **food** like **glucose** to growing parts of the plant.

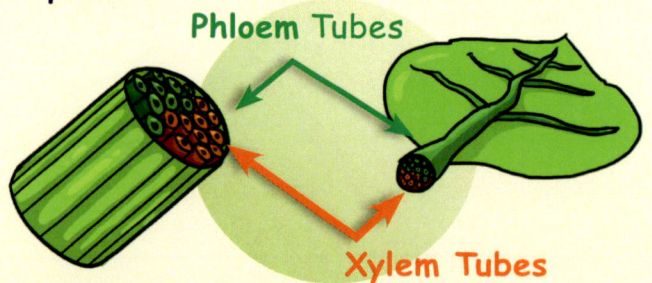

Phloem Tubes

Xylem Tubes

- **Xylem** tubes carry **water** and **minerals** around the plant.

Respiration & Photosynthesis

11   Respiration

- **All living things** carry out **respiration**.

  (Do you remember **MRS GREN?**
  Life Processes: Movement, Respiration, Sensitivity, Growth, Reproduction, Excretion, Nutrition).

- **Respiration** uses **glucose** and **oxygen** to release **energy**.

- The energy **released** comes from the **sunlight** that plants trap during **photosynthesis**.

Glucose **+** Oxygen (O_2) ➡ Carbon Dioxide (CO_2) **+** Water (H_2O) **+** Energy Released!

12   Respiration v. Photosynthesis

- All living things respire.

- **Respiration** uses **glucose** and oxygen.

- **Respiration** releases some of the energy trapped during photosynthesis.

- Plants **photosynthesise** and **respire**.

- **Photosynthesis** makes **glucose** and oxygen.

Energy Released

Respiration

Glucose **+** Oxygen (O_2) → Carbon Dioxide (CO_2) **+** Water (H_2O)

Photosynthesis

Energy stored

Plant Growth

13 The Good News!

- Plants make more **glucose** and oxygen than they use.

- The oxygen that we breathe is made by plants.

14 Life Depends on Plants!

- The food that we eat, or feed to the animals we eat, is made by plants.

- **Life on this planet depends upon plants.**

15 Minerals

- Plants need **minerals** to make molecules like **chlorophyll**.

- Plants get **minerals** from the soil.

- **Minerals** dissolve in water.

- They are taken up by the plant roots.

- Root hair cells increase the surface area.

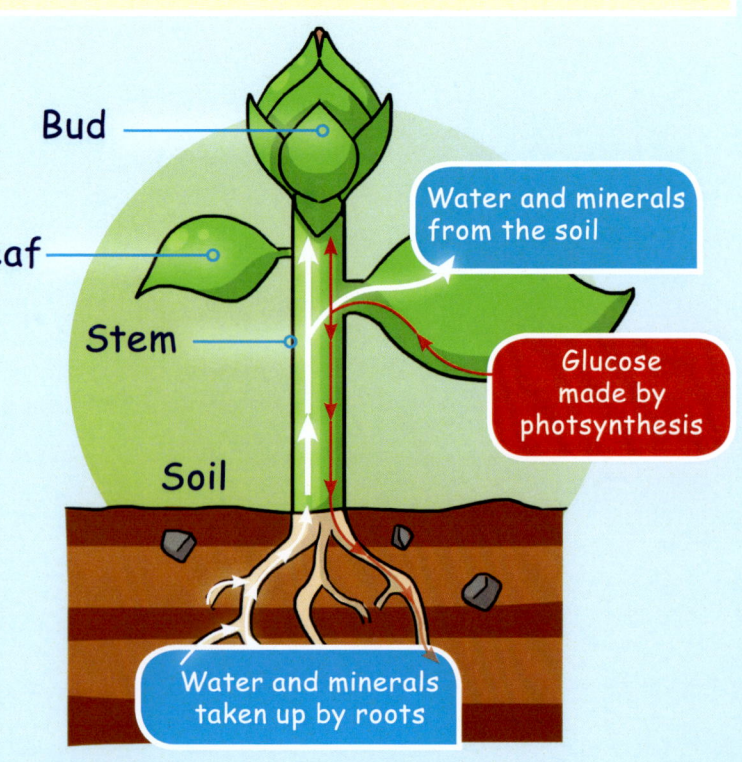

Bud

Leaf

Stem

Soil

Water and minerals from the soil

Glucose made by photsynthesis

Water and minerals taken up by roots

Using Glucose

16   Why Do Plants Need Glucose?

- **Respiration** (making energy).

- Making **cell walls**.

- Building molecules & proteins.

- **Glucose** is stored in seeds.

- **Glucose** is stored as **starch**.

17   Try This...

- Bread contains **starch**.

- Chew a piece of white **bread** for a long time.

- It begins to taste **sweet**.

- That's starch turning into **glucose**.

18   Plant Biomass

- As plants **photosynthesise** they grow.

- Some of the **glucose** they make is used for **respiration**.

- The **glucose** left over is stored. This is used for growth.

- Plant **biomass** is plant matter.

Bigger Plant = More Biomass

19   Do Plants Sweat?

- Animals sweat by losing water.

- Plants lose water too. It is called **transpiration**.

- Plants lose water through their **stomata**.

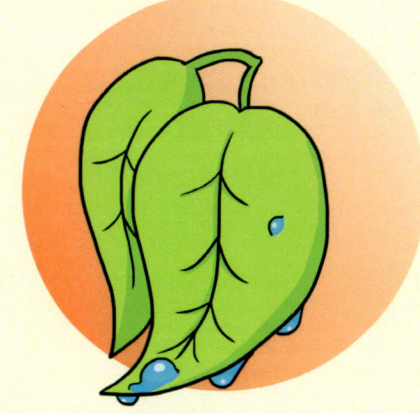

Plant Growth

20   Waterproof

- Leaves have a waxy layer (**wax cuticle**) on the top.

- This helps stop water loss.

- Leaves do not have many **stomata** on the top surface.

21   Night & Day

- **Photosynthesis** needs light. So it only happens in the day.

- **Respiration** happens **all the time.**

- On a cloudy day **photosynthesis** slows down.

- In the winter, when it's dark and cold, plant growth slows or stops.

22   Greenhouses

Plants grown in greenhouses get lots of light all the time.

- Greenhouses are often heated using **fossil fuels**. Which gas is given off when **fossil fuels burn**?

Hint: it's the same gas that's produced during respiration.

23   Plants Like to be Warm

- All living things use **enzymes.**

- **Enzymes** are **biological catalysts.**

- They speed up chemical reactions .

Faster!! Faster!!

Plants & Photosynthesis

24 Plants Like to be Warm

- Respiration is a **chemical reaction**.

- Chemical reactions happen **faster** when it is **warm**.

- Plants grow quicker→more biomass

25 Minerals

- The **minerals** that plants take from the soil may get used up if you grow too many plants in **one place**.

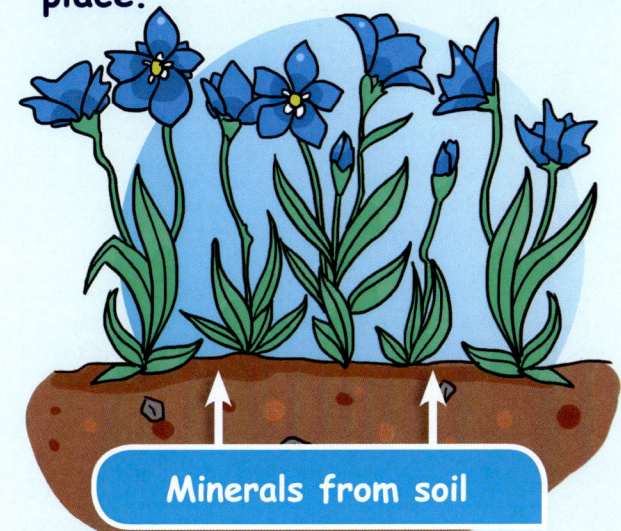

Minerals from soil

26 Fertilisers

- The **rock cycle, nitrogen cycle** and **carbon cycle** all help to put these **minerals** back.

- But not always fast enough.

Farmers may use **NPK fertilisers** to put minerals back fast.

27 Sick Plants!

- Plants use **nitrates** for making plant **protein**.

- Not enough **nitrate** = poor growth.

- **Magnesium** is used for making **chlorophyll**. Too little and the leaves turn yellow!

Plants & Photosynthesis

28   Healthy Plants' Shopping List...

Healthy plants need...

- **Fertile soil** with lots of **minerals.**

- **Water** to make cells rigid and stop plants wilting.

- **Water, carbon dioxide** and **sunlight** for **photosynthesis.**

- **Warmth** to speed growth.

29   Soil

- Plants **do not** use up the soil.

- Plants use **minerals** and **water** from the soil.

Soil with **minerals**   Soil without **minerals**

30   Types of Soil

There are different types of soil.....

- Clay (small bits)

- Sandy (bigger bits)

- Loam (mixture of big and small particles).

- Loam soil is best for plants.

31   Testing Plant Growth

- Measure two plants.

- Put one in sunlight with water and warmth.

- Put the other in the dark with water and warmth.

- Measure the growth.

Plants & Water

32   Loosing Water

- Plants have lots of **stomata** on the bottom of the leaf.

- They let gases in and out.

- They also let water out by **transpiration.**

Only gas and water past us.

33   Losing water

- Large leaves lose lots of water.

- Small leaves lose only a small amount of water.

34   Different Leaves

- Cacti have very small leaves (needles).

- They lose only a small amount of water. They grow very slowly.

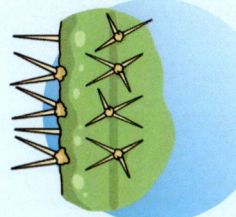

- Water lillies have big leaves.

- They grow fast, why?

Clue: **photosynthesis.**

35   Finding Water

- Plants take up water through their **root hair cells**.

- Plants living in dry places have deep roots to find water.

- Plants living in wet places usually have shallow roots.

Deep Roots   Shallow Roots

Plants & Photosynthesis

36   Plants for Food

- **Glucose** made during **photosynthesis** can be found in fruit like oranges.

- **Glucose** is stored as **starch**.

- Potatoes contain a lot of starch.

37   Energy from Sunlight

- The **energy from sunlight**, captured by plants during photosynthesis, is the **source** of **all life** on Earth.

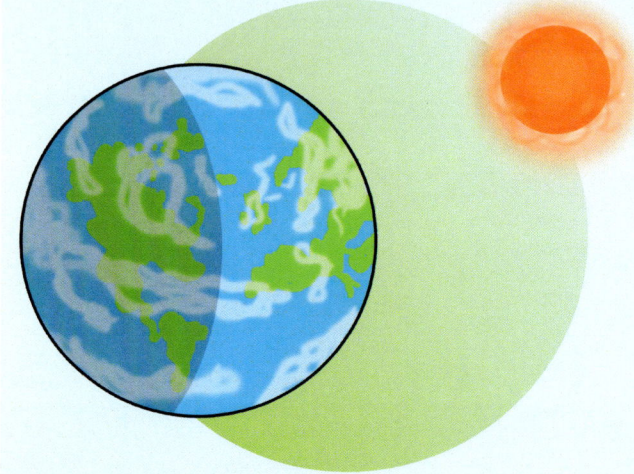

38   Biofuels

- The **glucose** from plants can be used to make **alcohol**.

- **Alcohol** can be used as a **fuel** for cars. This is a **biofuel**.

- Wood burning stoves use biofuel!

39   The Future

- **Crude oil** is running out.

- **Biofuels** are already being used to run cars.

40 Plants and the Air

The air before plants...

- Mostly **carbon dioxide** with little or **no oxygen.**

- Made from the gases given out by volcanoes.

The air with plants...

- A **tiny amount** of carbon dioxide (about 0.04%).

- Lots of **oxygen** (about 21%).

- Mostly nitrogen (78%).

41 How Much CO_2?

One single big tree uses about 22kg of carbon dioxide per year during **photosynthesis**!

CO_2
22KG

It takes about 22 trees to make enough oxygen for you to breathe each year!

O_2

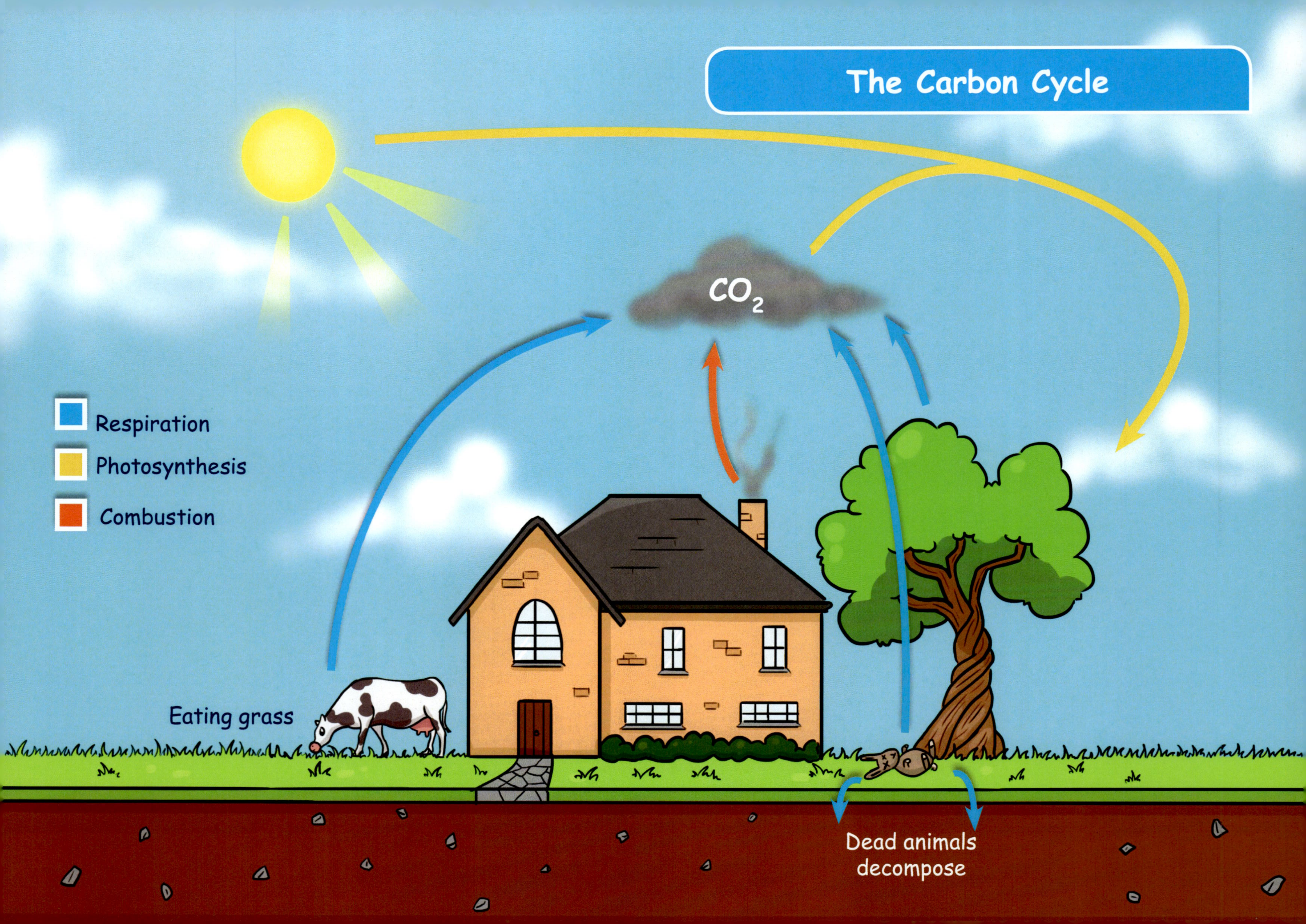

The Carbon Cycle

CO_2

Respiration

Photosynthesis

Combustion

Eating grass

Dead animals decompose

Important!

Differences Between Plant & Animal Cells

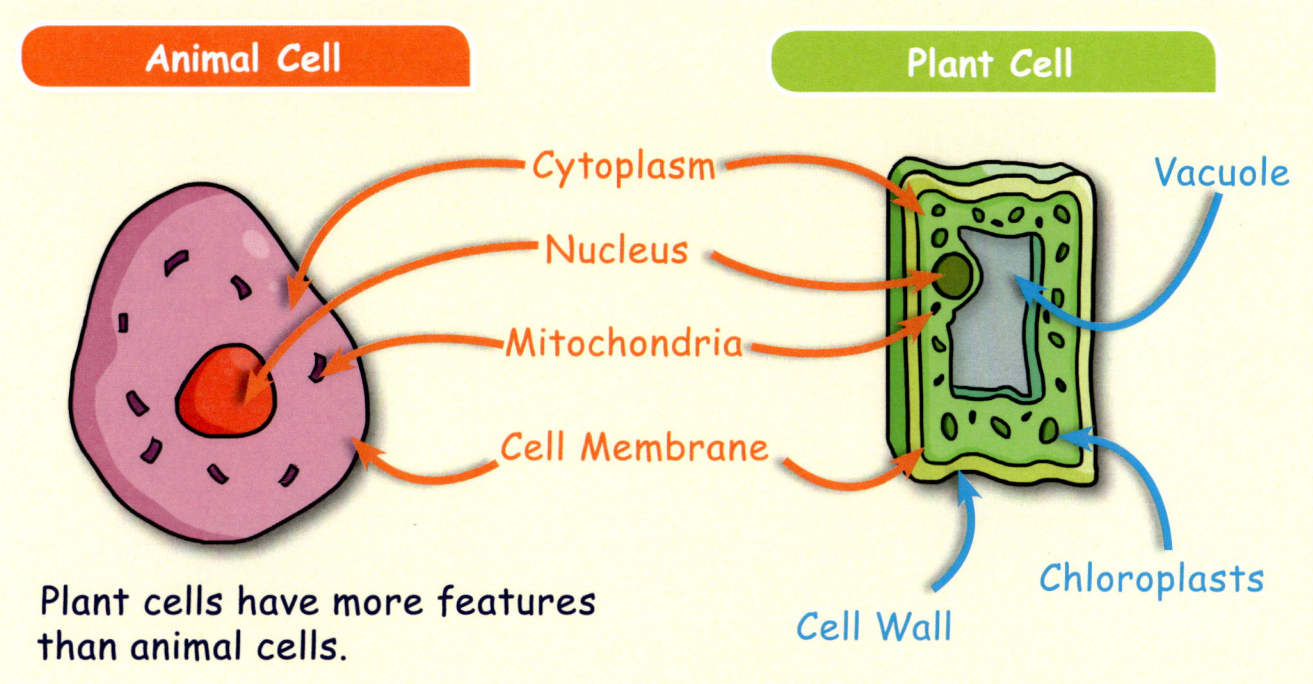

Animal Cell

Plant Cell

Cytoplasm

Nucleus

Mitochondria

Cell Membrane

Vacuole

Chloroplasts

Cell Wall

Plant cells have more features than animal cells.

What is in the Air?

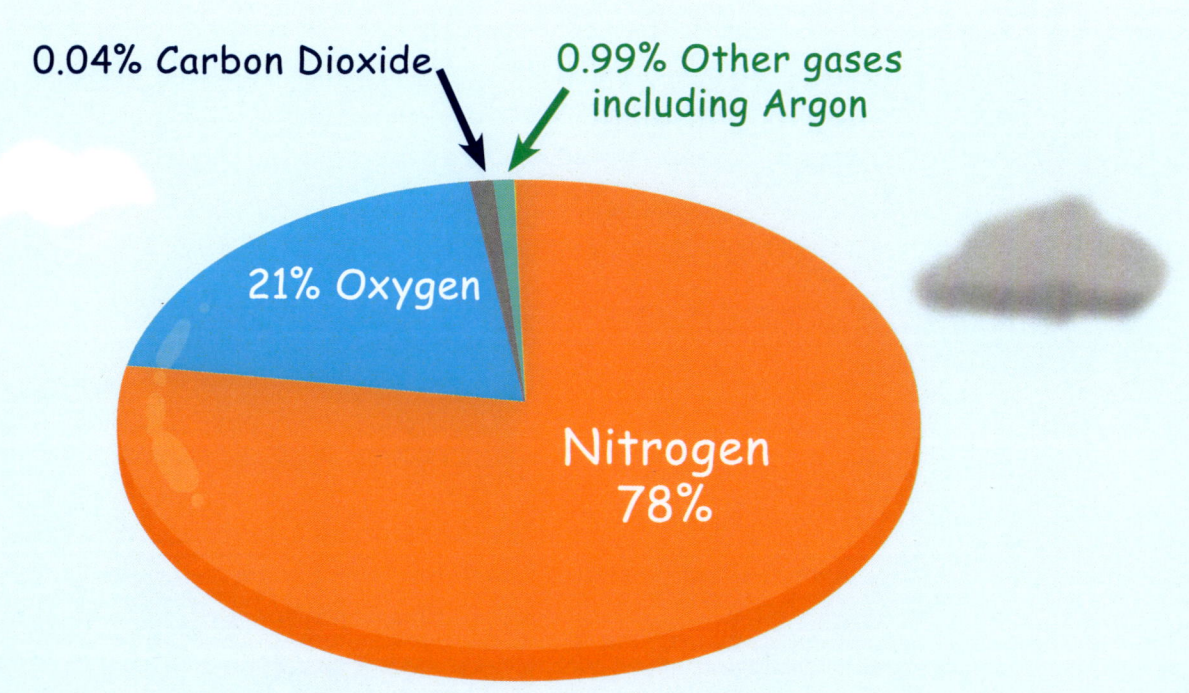

0.04% Carbon Dioxide

0.99% Other gases including Argon

21% Oxygen

Nitrogen 78%

Test for Starch in a Leaf

A   Leaf in Boiling Water

- **Put a leaf in boiling water for about 60 seconds.**
- Remove it with tongs.

Be careful! Only carry out this test under the instruction of a teacher.

B   Leaf in Ethanol

- Half fill a boiling tube with **ethanol**.
- Put the leaf into the ethanol.
- Stand the boiling tube in **hot** (not boiling) water for 10 minutes.

Ethanol (Put leaf in here)

Stand in hot water

Make sure there are no naked flames as ethanol burns easily!

C   Leaf in Hot Water

- Using tongs, put the leaf into the **hot water** to soak.
- Leave it for 60 seconds.

Put leaf in hot water

D   Iodine Solution on Leaf

- Using tongs, lay the leaf **flat** on a white ceramic tile.
- Drip **iodine solution** all over the leaf.

Drip iodine solution on leaf

- The iodine solution will turn **blue/black** if there is **starch** present.

  Don't forget! For experiments always wear safety googles and a apron.

Leaf Cross Section

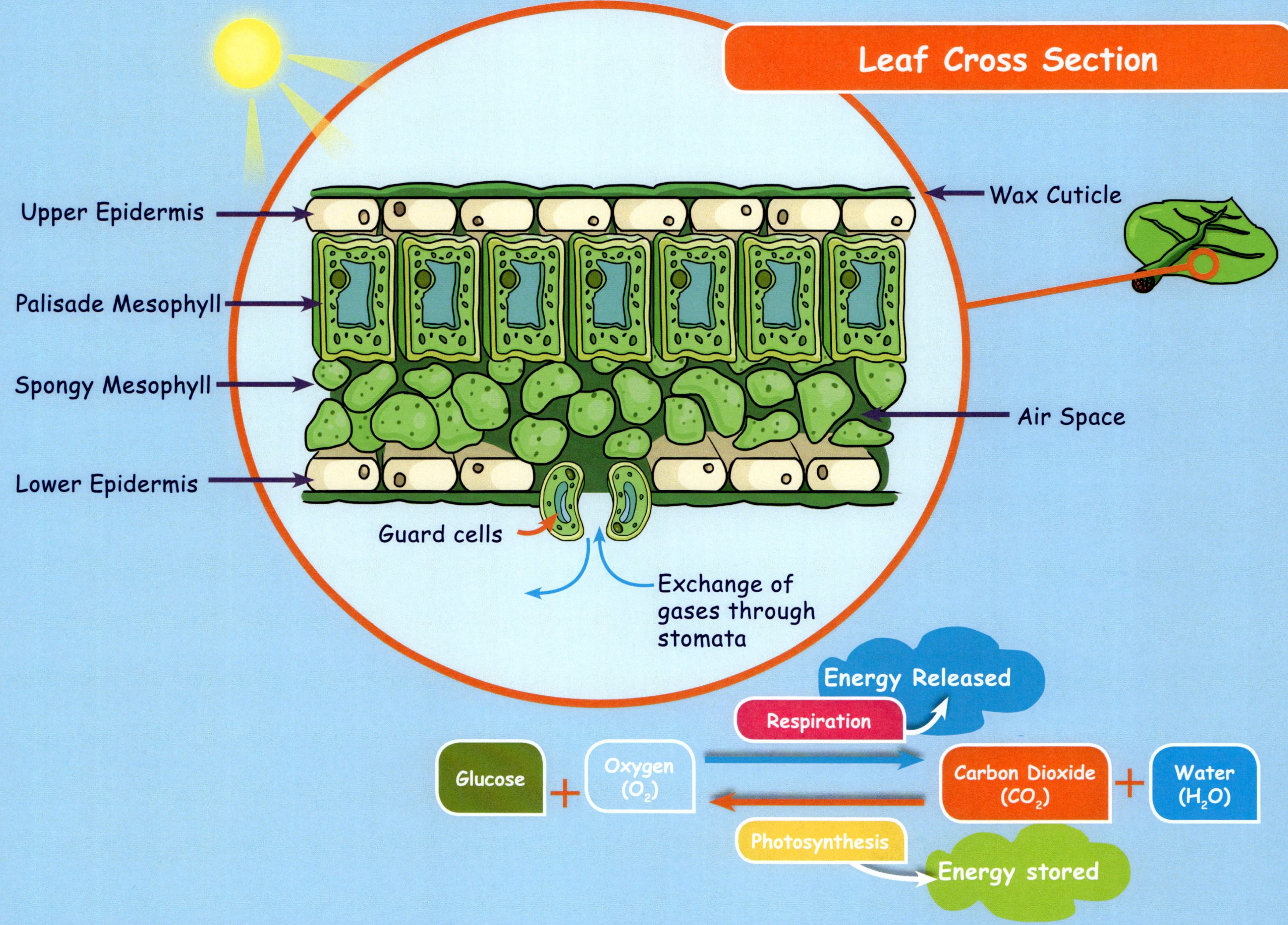

Wax Cuticle

Air Space

Exchange of gases through stomata

Guard cells

Upper Epidermis

Palisade Mesophyll

Spongy Mesophyll

Lower Epidermis

Water (H₂O)

Carbon Dioxide (CO₂)

Energy stored

Energy Released

Respiration

Photosynthesis

Oxygen (O₂)

Glucose

About Oaka Books

Children learn best when they are engaged...

Our aim is to help children enjoy learning by making it fun! That way they will succeed.

Following Common Entrance and National Curriculum guidelines for KS3.

Design and layout of our books follow guidelines from the British Dyslexia Association

Three Easy Steps

Read: the easy to follow bullet point Topic Booklet.

Engage: Play the Active Learning Game.

Learn: When you understand the topic, test yourself using the Write Your Own Notes Book. You can use the Topic Booklet to help if you get stuck.

One (short) Topic at a time:

For some students, a big book is a big turn off. That's why we focus on one topic at a time. Short and to the point.

Reading Age

This booklet is suitable for children with a reading age of 10 ½ years.

Topic Packs for KS1, KS2 & KS3 Include:

History
Geography
Chemistry
Biology
Physics
French
Maths

First paperback edition printed 2015 in the United Kingdom.
A catalogue record for this book is available from the British Library.

ISBN 978-1-909892-55-2
No part of this book shall be reproduced or transmitted in any form or by any means, electronic or mechanical, including photocopying, recording or by any information retrieval system without written permission of the copyright owner or a licence permitting restricted copying issued by the Copyright Licensing Agency Ltd, Saffron House, 6-10 Kirby Street, London EC1N 8TS Tel: 020 7400 3100   Fax: 020 7400 3101   Email: cla@cla.co.uk   Web: www.cla.co.uk

Designed, set and published by Oaka™ Books.

To order other titles from Oaka™ Books, please email info@oakabooks.co.uk or visit www.oakabooks.co.uk, or phone: +44 (023) 92 388519.

Acknowledgements
Our huge thanks go to the many teachers who have been involved in the development of this series of learning guides. Special thanks to Joy Gardiner, for producing hundreds of illustrations, to Kate Doehren, for her enthusiasm and invaluable assistance to my wonderful daughter Sophie, for being the inspiration for the books and, of course, to Charlie, for believing in them.

ISBN 978-1-909892-55-2

CE/KS3
Plants & Photosyn-

Topic Booklet